Nan's Man

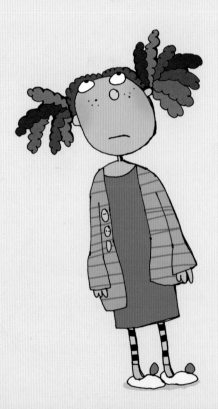

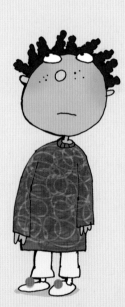

Written by Nicola Sandford

Illustrated by Jess Mikhail

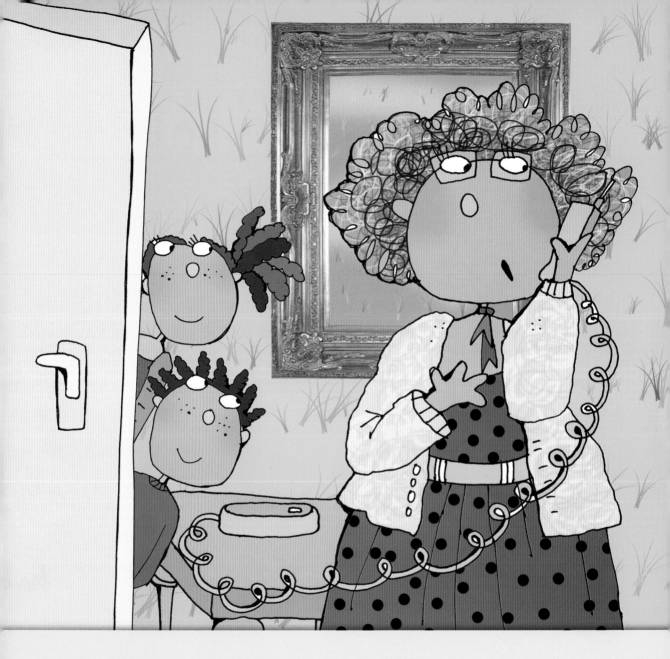

Nan is in a panic.

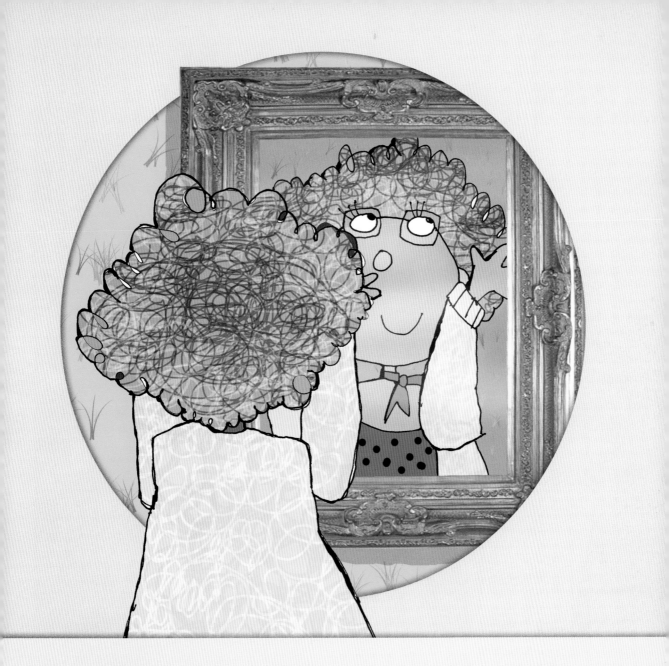

"Jim will visit me."

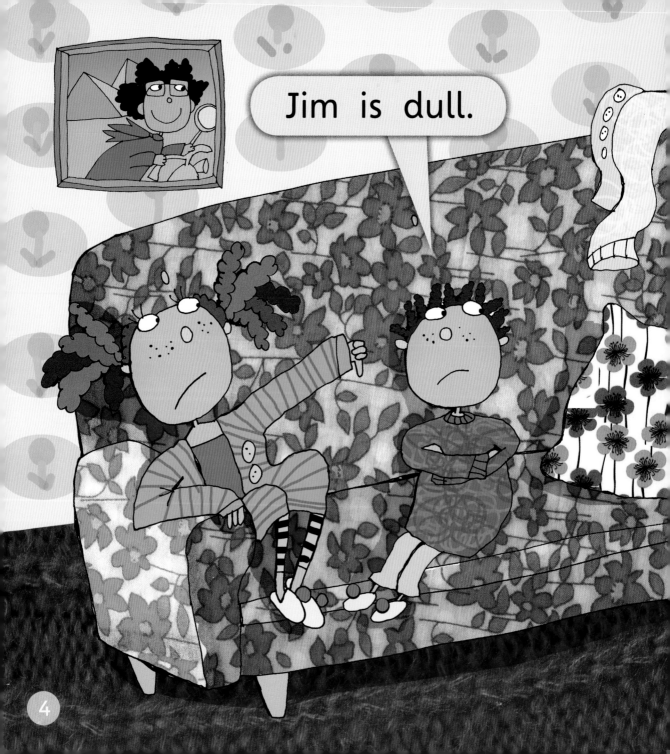

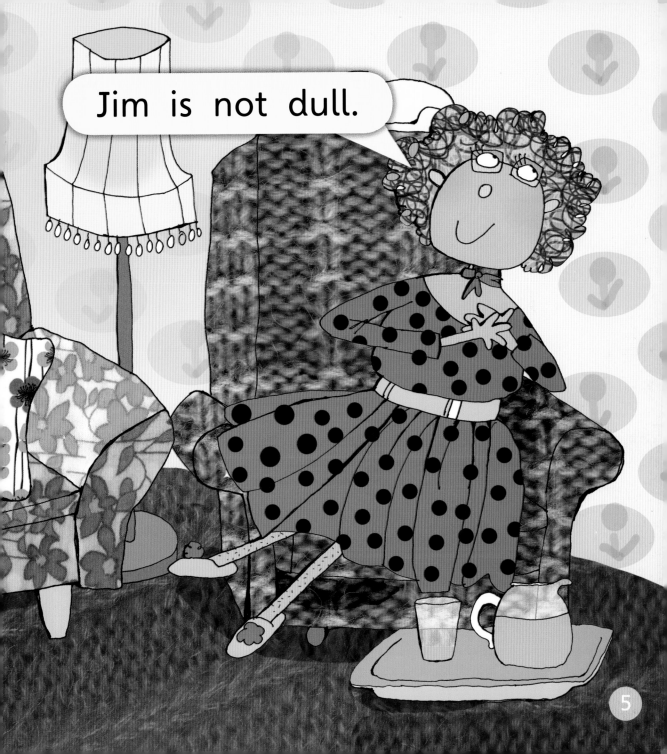

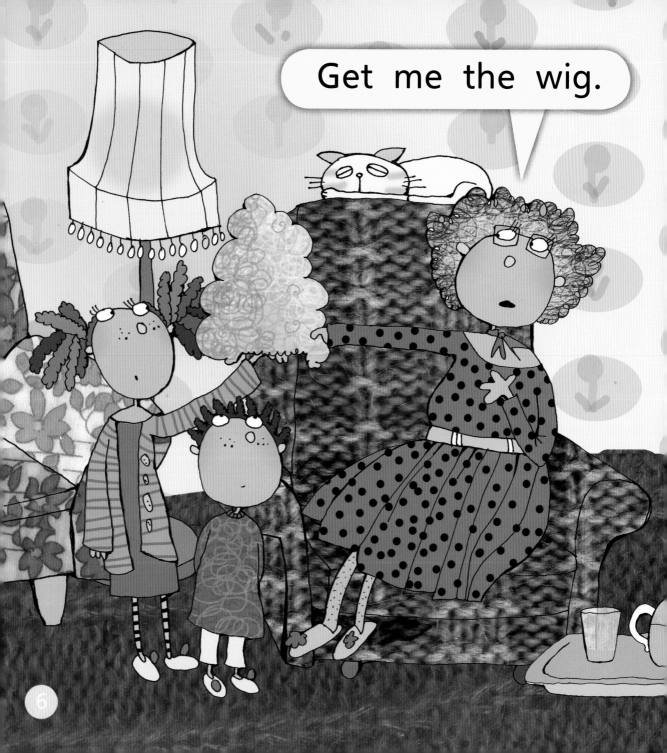

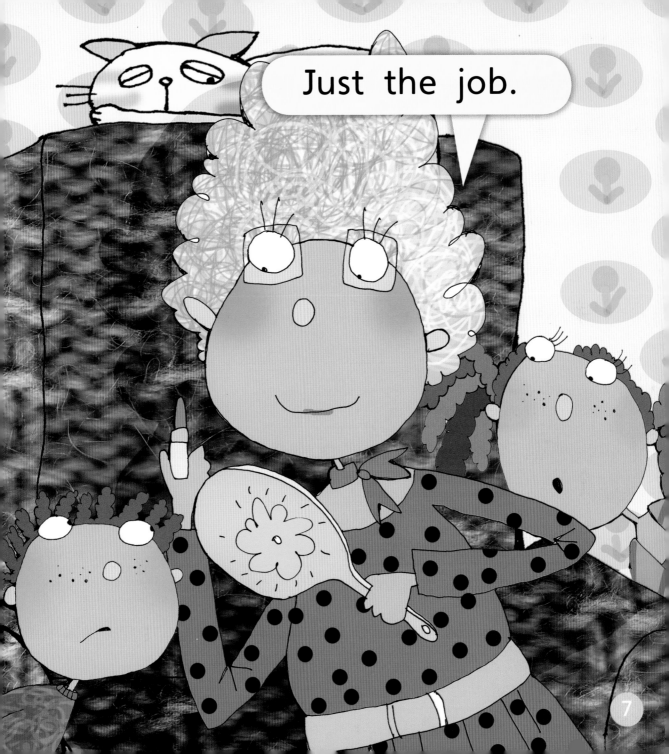

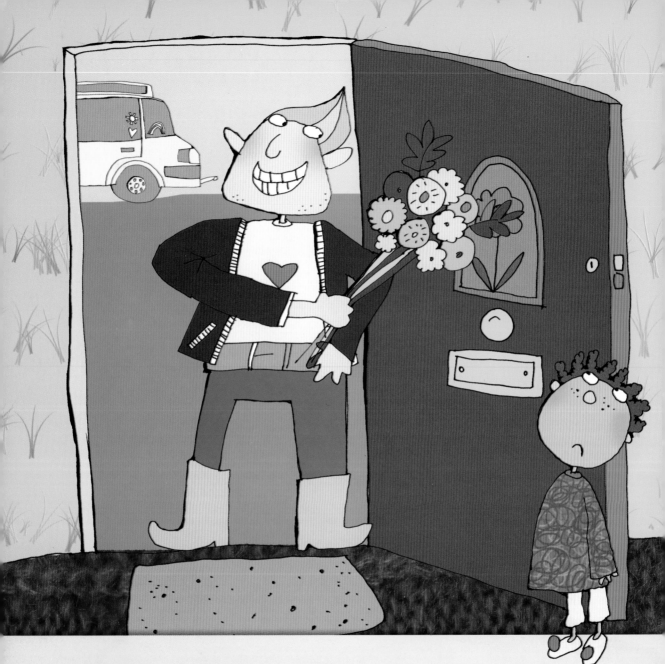

Jim visits.

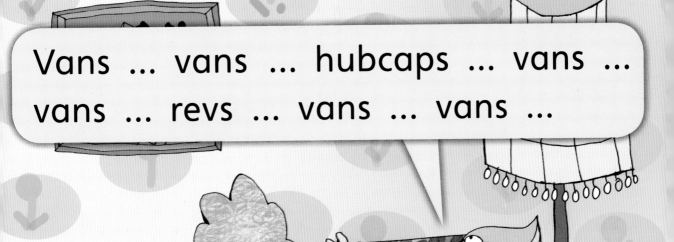

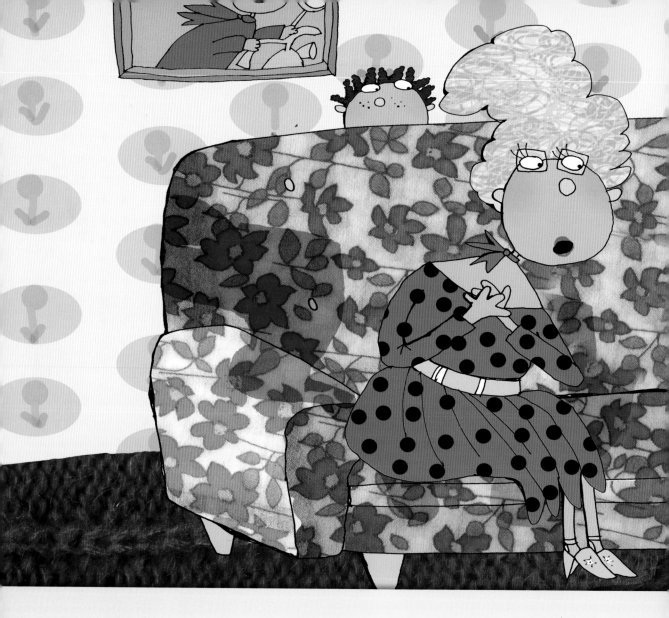

Jim has a box.

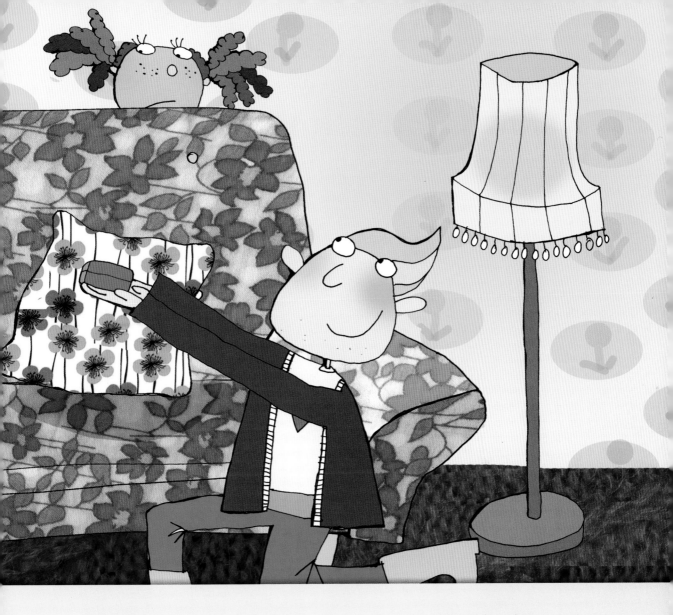

Will Jim win Nan's hand?
Will Jim be Nan's man?

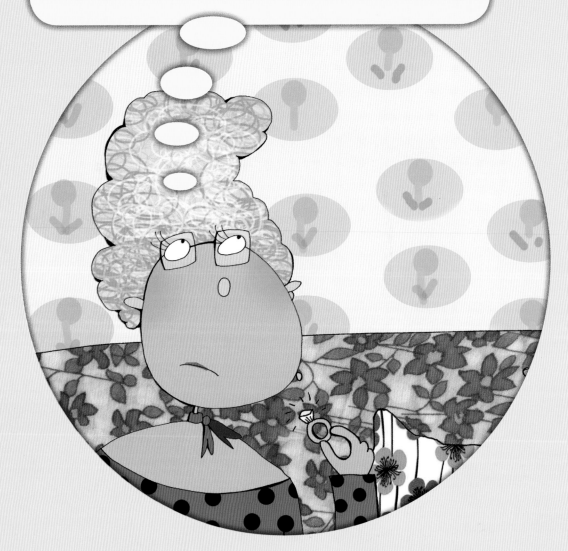

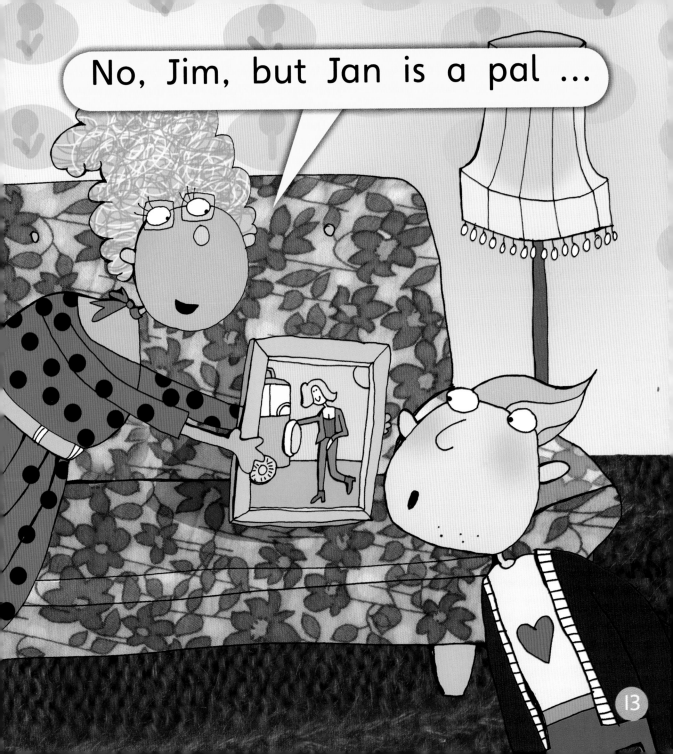

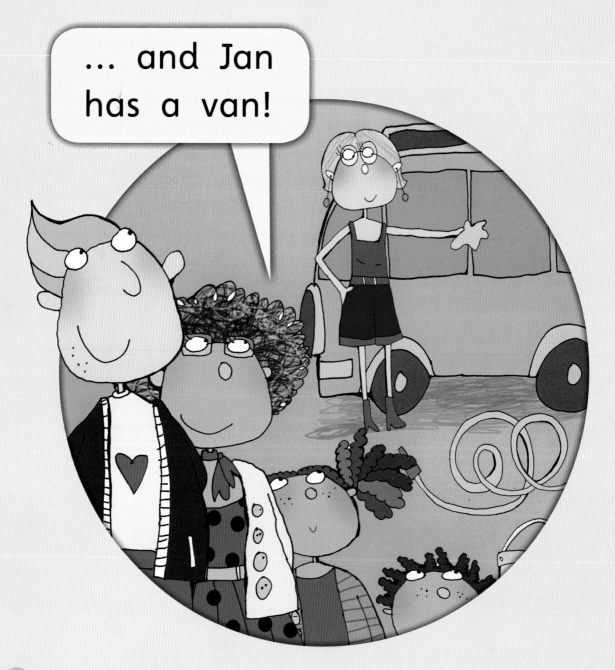

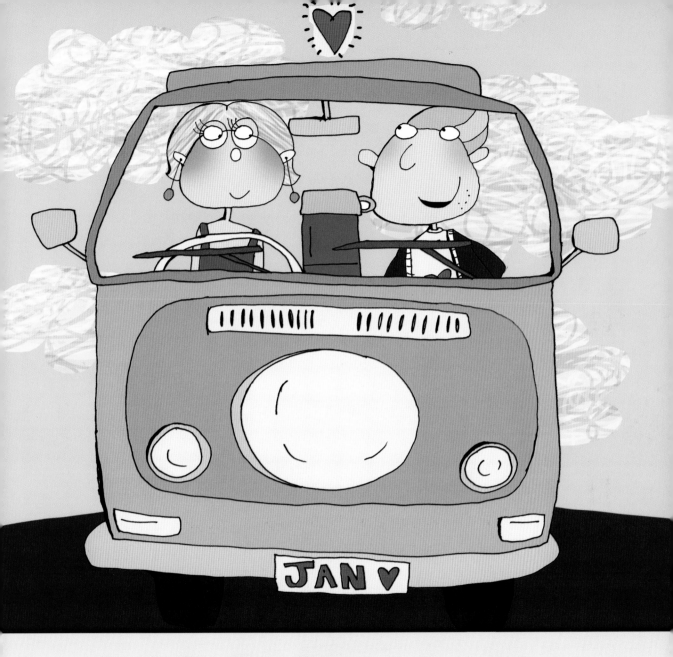

"I will be Jan's man!"

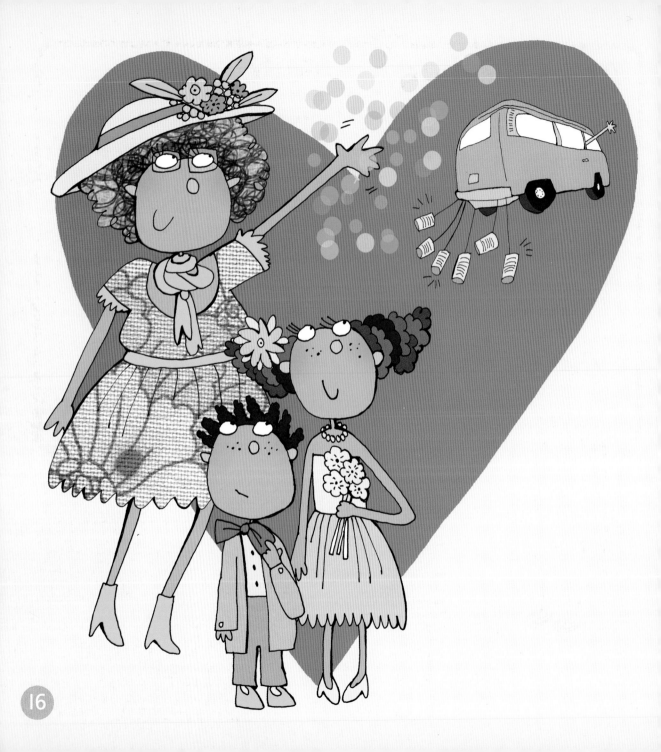